Jazztastic.

The progressive, play-as-you-learn guide
to jazz improvisation and soloing

Piano
Initial Level

International MUSIC Publications

International Music Publications Limited
Griffin House 161 Hammersmith Road London W6 8BS England

**DON'T BE
A MUSIC
COPYCAT!**

The copying of © copyright
material is a criminal offence
and may lead to prosecution.

Series Editor: Sadie Cook

Editorial, production and recording: Artemis Music Limited
Design and production: Space DPS Limited
Photographs courtesy of Redferns Music Picture Library - Booker T and The
MGs (page 11) - CA; Count Basie (page 15) - David Redfern; Charlie Parker
(page 32) - William Gottlieb; Henry Mancini (page 35) - Suzi Gibbons

Piano: Liam Noble
Rhythm section on the CD: Liam Noble (piano); Andy Hamil (bass); Tom Gordon (d

Published 1999

**International
MUSIC
Publications**

IMP

International Music Publications Limited

England:	Griffin House 161 Hammersmith Road London W6 8BS
Germany:	Marstallstr. 8 D-80539 München
Denmark:	Danmusik Vognmagergade 7 DK1120 Copenhagen K

Carisch

Italy:	Via Campania 12 20098 San Giuliano Milanese Milano
Spain:	Magallanes 25 28015 Madrid
France:	20 Rue de la Ville-l'Eveque 75008 Paris

Jazztastic!

Piano
Initial Level

In the Book...

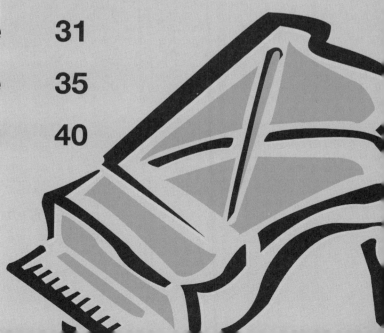

Jazztastic!

On the CD...

introduction

Welcome to Jazztastic! - the playalong series that goes the extra mile to help you with your jazz improvisation and soloing. Not only does the accompanying CD use the classic jazz rhythm section line-up of piano, bass and drums for you to play along to, but there is also a complete demonstration track of each piece for you to hear. This demonstration track gives an opportunity for you to hear a professional jazz musician play their own solos over the tracks that you will use. You can listen to these tracks for your own pleasure, just as you would with any other of your favourite albums, or you can use them to study from as a source of inspiration and new ideas.

To help you take on board the music you hear on the demonstration tracks, this book provides the first chorus of every solo written out in full. In this way you can learn to play the sample solo from music notation whilst also acquiring vocabulary and ideas. At the end of each piece you will find some 'Rhythmic Ideas'. Here we have taken two bars from the sample solo and developed the ideas by using different rhythms and phrase structures. These show how the melodic ideas used in the sample solo can be adapted to create new ideas.

Try writing out your own examples and see in how many ways you can re-invent one simple idea. All of these helpful hints and additional information will also help to demystify the process of making up a melodic line from the chord changes, as you will see how the solo picks out the important harmonic notes of the sequence.

You might like to try playing along with piano player Liam Noble on the demonstration track - this will allow you to experiment with picking out some of his ideas by ear on your instrument. Many of the most important figures in jazz music learnt to play by copying the solos that they heard on recordings and this is a great opportunity for you to do the same.

As well as the sample solo, we also give you the tune written out with a set ending to follow. There is also space on the page for you to write in your own solo ideas while scale resources and melodic ideas are all written out for you. The scale resources are there to help you understand the melodic properties of the harmonic sequence. We suggest that you use them as a practice aid rather than trying to read them while soloing. Remember that they are there as a resource to be learnt rather than as something to rely on if you can't think of anything to play. Where there is more than one chord in the bar we have often provided just a chord voicing rather than the whole scale. This is because we think it is more practical for you to outline some basic voice-leading movement, as the harmony moves quite swiftly at these points.

Before each piece we give some background information, including potted biographical details of the composers and suggested listening, along with an insight into the historical context. Helpful hints on style and interpretation are given, along with highlighted points to listen out for.

Using only a selection of popular jazz standards and well-known instrumental hits as repertoire, Jazztastic! is a fun playalong approach to improvisation and a jazz album rolled into one.

C Jam Blues

Duke Ellington was one of the great American band leaders and jazz composers. He had a variety of bands throughout his career and perfected the art of writing very well for specific musicians, often getting the best out of them as soloists, but in a group context. His way of writing also involved every member of his band, making the ensemble playing perfectly suited to each player. Very often the players themselves would come up with the basic ideas for 'riffs' - simple musical ideas that work across a complete chord sequence with minimal alteration.

The Arrangement

C Jam Blues is based entirely on one riff, making it easy to learn and fun to play. The tune itself is made up of only two notes, always played in the same rhythmic 'shape'. Once you have learned the first four bars of the tune, you know the whole thing!

So what's the point of having such a simple (and short) little tune? Well for a start it allows everyone to join in straight away with the minimum of fuss. Secondly, it allows space for the arrangement to be built up around the tune, and thirdly it makes an ideal vehicle for soloing over.

After a short introduction you are straight into the Head, or main melody, of the piece. The Head is played twice, after which the solos start. The first chorus is written out for you, but on the subsequent ones you are free to make up your own solo. There are four choruses of the solo, with backing figures coming in on the third and final times to tell you where you are.

The Soloing

The chord sequence is the classic 12-bar blues. This has to be one of the most common chord sequences in music, whether jazz, rock, blues, or pop. There is a whole musical tradition based on these three simple chords, and here we give you an introduction to how the form works.

There are three main sections in a 12-bar, each of which is four bars long. The first section gives you four bars of the home key, in this case C. The next four bars take you to the fourth degree of the home scale (the sub-dominant) for two bars, then back home again for another two. So, in this instance you have two bars of F followed by two bars of C.

Look at the chord sequence of the head on page 8. The final four bars *usually* have one bar of the dominant, or fifth degree (G), followed by one bar of the sub-dominant (F) before going home (to C) for the remaining two bars. Then the sequence starts all over again, and so on.

So much for the form of the chord sequence, but what can you play over it that will sound good? We have already given you one complete chorus of a written out solo. This will be fun to play and will give you some ideas for creating your own solo.

Here is a scale that works well over all three chords. It is full of 'bluesy' sounds and intervals, and will enable you to play around with patterns over the whole sequence whilst feeling perfectly secure.

Track 1: The Blues scale on C

Blues scale on C

"... it don't mean a thing if, it ain't got that swing..."
Duke Ellington

Listen to the demonstration of the Blues scale on track 1 of the CD, then play it for yourself. Don't just go up and down the six notes, but start making patterns with it. It's only when you've achieved some sort of dexterity and familiarity with the scale that you will feel comfortable in using it to solo with.

Now that you feel comfortable with the Blues scale, which works over the whole progression, let's look at some other scale choices. Underneath the sample solo are written some more scales. These are melodic resources for you to use as well as the Blues scale These are all what are called 'Mixolydian' scales, which, in theoretical terms means the 'fifth mode' of the major scale. Another way of looking at it is to think of the Mixolydian scale as being the same as the major scale with a flattened 7th. This is no coincidence since the chord type C^7 is basically a major triad with a ♭7 on top. So here we have a good relationship between the melodic resources and the chord type. This is a very important concept to grasp as an improvising musician.

Here are the Mixolydian scales written out for you to practise. Try to find patterns made up from the notes in the scale and pick the more colourful notes to use in your improvisations. Lastly, we must notice that as there are three different scales to use, there will be notes common to all three, but also notes that only occur in a particular scale.

The following example is the chord sequence played with particular reference to these important different notes. This is also referred to as the 'guide tone' sequence which will be explained further in later chapters of the book.

Track 2: 'Guide Tone' sequence

Suggested listening...

Here is a list of recordings that are relevant to this piece. This is not an exhaustive or comprehensive list, but it will give you a starting point.

DUKE ELLINGTON & HIS ORCHESTRA
EARLY ELLINGTON   (BLUEBIRD)

DUKE ELLINGTON & HIS ORCHESTRA
THE INDISPENSABLE VOLS 5/6   (RCA)

DUKE ELLINGTON & HIS ORCHESTRA
AT NEWPORT   (COLUMBIA)

DUKE ELLINGTON & HIS ORCHESTRA
THE FAR EAST SUITE   (BLUEBIRD)

a) mixolydian on C

b) mixolydian on F

c) mixolydian on G

C Jam Blues

Duke Ellington

By Duke Ellington

Light swing ♩ = 114

Rhythmic ideas for bars 2 and 3
of the Solo Section

Green Onions

This is the famous instrumental hit from 1963 by Booker T and the MGs. The group represented what came to be a distinct brand of soul music called 'Memphis Soul' which was a rival to the increasingly popular 'Motown' sound. The band included guitarist Steve Cropper, organist Booker T. Jones, bassist Lewis Steinberg and drummer Al Jackson who all later became the regular rhythm section for Otis Redding. In fact guitarist Steve Cropper co-wrote Otis Redding's best selling hit *Sitting On The Dock Of The Bay* as well as numerous other commercial successes such as *In The Midnight Hour* and *Soul Man*.

The Arrangement

This is a classic 12-bar blues progression but this time in a minor key. There is a very simple repeated bass line throughout and some important rhythm section figures. For the introduction you can join in with these 'hits' or 'pushes' as they are sometimes called. See if you can catch them with the rhythm section in the 12 bars before the Head starts. Here is an example of how this 'kick' fits with the bass line.

Track 5: Hits with bass line

You can also think of this as playing on the 'and' of beat four.

When playing the Head you will notice that some of the phrases have grace notes within them. These are important stylistic inflections but they can be tricky to get your fingers round at first. Why not try just playing the melody straight first of all and then add the grace notes once you feel comfortable with the basic framework of the tune? Also notice that the groove is a type of rock shuffle meaning that the quaver feel is not a straight eighth division but is approaching a dotted quaver/semi-quaver feel. There are long and short phrase markings on the part to help you.

After you have played the Head for the last time there is a fade out on the F minor chord like the original recording. You can either solo here or play the 'hits' as in the introduction. You can of course do a bit of both!

The Soloing

The soloing style here should be sparse and very bluesy. You may like to try using ideas directly from the Head like the soloists on the original recording. This may involve playing phrases from the Head in slightly different places rhythmically, or maybe using different notes but the same rhythm. Either way, notice how much space is left between the phrases of the Head and the sample solo. This is very much in keeping with the style, that is, the soloist allows plenty of space for the listener to enjoy the groove coming from the rest of the band. Leaving so much space also draws the listener in because they are waiting with anticipation for your next phrase.

The notes written out below the sample solo for you to use in your own improvisations are in fact minor pentatonics. These are useful melodic resources for your soloing and are worth practising separately to gain a bit of dexterity with them.

You can of course use the blues scale throughout the whole sequence. Notice how similar this F blues scale is to the F minor pentatonic. Here is the F blues scale written out.

Track 6: The F Blues Scale

Have a look at the Head and the sample solo and see how many of the notes used are from the blues scale.

> " ... each musician is based on someone who went before, and eventually you get enough of your own things... and you get a style of your own... "
>
> Dizzy Gillespie

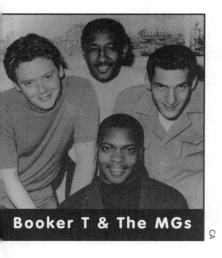

Booker T & The MGs

Green Onions

Booker T and the MGs

By Booker T Jones, Steve Cropper, Lewie Steinberg
and Al Jackson Jnr

Rock shuffle ♩ = 132

Introduction

Rhythmic ideas for bars 6 and 7
of the Solo Section

One O'Clock Jump

*O*ne O'Clock Jump was Count Basie's first ever hit, recorded in 1937 on the Decca label. It was played on juke boxes across the United States and established him and his band as one of the leading jazz groups of the time.

Count Basie formed his band out of musicians playing in and around Kansas City in the early 1930s. His music was consequently steeped in the authentic blues tradition and was full of riffs and collective improvising. In fact a lot of the early arrangements for the Basie orchestra were composed collectively. Different sections of the band would make up their own ideas to fit in with other elements of the arrangement. These would include backings for the soloists as well as the main themes.

The Arrangement

For this arrangement we've given you a couple of the main riffing themes to play. *One O`Clock Jump* is really a collection of interlocking rhythmic ideas played by a Big Band, but to play this tune with a small jazz group you can use these two distinctive themes. You will find that for the whole length of a chorus one simple idea is repeated. This is essentially what a riff is – a repeated rhythmic motif, usually blues based, that allows you just to have fun swinging along with the rhythm section.

When Basie played this tune he would start everyone off by playing a few choruses of blues in the key of F. However, the arrangement is in the key of D♭. This is a great idea, because when the band comes in, it sounds like everyone has gone up a gear. The track you will here on the CD uses the same device, with a chorus of piano in F before the Heads and solos in D♭.

The Soloing

Count Basie

David Redfern

This is another 12-bar blues here in the somewhat unusual key of D♭. Other D♭ blues that you are likely to encounter in this style are *Splanky* and *Wood Choppers Ball*. The chord changes follow the normal format for a 12-bar blues. It can be broken down into three four-bar sections, the first starting on the home chord, the second starting on chord IV, and the last starting on chord V. These key centres are called the tonic, subdominant and dominant respectively, and are important harmonic movements in the blues sequence.

You can pick out these harmonic movements by aiming for the guide tones in your melodic line. The example below shows the chord types and the guide tones together.

Look at how the riffs used for the Head of this arrangement are modified slightly to fit in with the guide tones. In bar five of the first Head for instance, we have an F♭ instead of an F♮ to fit with the guide tones of G♭7. Similarly, in bar nine of the second Head, you will see that the riff idea finishes up on a G♭, which is the all important guide tone of A♭7. By learning these two riffs you will be learning how to outline the harmonic movement in a blues sequence.

Once you feel comfortable with these important chord tones you can move on to using the Mixolydian scales written out below the sample solo. Remember that you can also use the blues scale throughout the entire sequence. Here is the D♭ blues scale written out.

If you've heard the original version of *One O'Clock Jump* you will notice that there are many other riffs that the band uses throughout the arrangement. These simple ideas will work throughout the whole sequence. Try playing the following examples over the backing track and have fun digging in with the rhythm section.

 Tracks 9/10/11: Backing riffs

" *... what makes the style is not what you play, but how you play it...* "

Dizzy Gillespie

One O'Clock Jump

Count Basie

By Count Basie

Jive ♩ = 160

Summertime

George Gershwin

This is one of Gershwin's most memorable and evocative tunes that has become a firm favourite as a jazz standard. It comes originally from the opera 'Porgy and Bess', written in 1935, which includes other famous tunes such as *I Got Plenty Of Nuttin'* and *I Loves You Porgy*.

The Arrangement

In its original form *Summertime* is a vocal ballad with a slow lilting tempo. However, in a jazz setting the possibilities for interpretation become wide open. The tune is so strong and instantly recognisable that virtually any stylistic approach will work. There have been Latin or funk versions of this tune as well as gospel, rock and swing.

This arrangement is in four crotchets to the bar at a hard driving swing tempo. This lends itself well to the improvising as it invites a good use of blues notes and allows the soloist to stretch out a little more than otherwise.

The length of one chorus is 16 bars, which can be thought of as four lots of four bar sections. The first and third lots of four bars use the same phrase of the tune and are harmonically identical while the second and fourth lots of four bars are different from the rest of the sequence. We can describe this form as being an ABAC form. As an improvising jazz musician it's very useful to be able to understand the form of the tune that you are soloing on. As you are making up your own ideas rather than following a written line it is very easy to lose your way unless you can hear the form. Listen to the track a few times without playing and follow the form of the piece as outlined below. See if you can hear and feel the four bar phrase lengths and get a sense of beginning, middle and end to the form as a whole. Once you feel comfortable with this you can free yourself to listen to the rhythm section more or concentrate on your melodic lines.

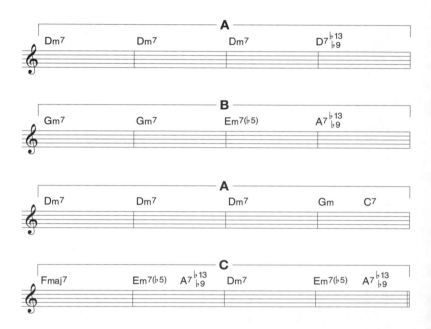

The Soloing

The sequence is based around D minor with quite a bluesy feel to it. This blues feel is created by a characteristic movement to chord IV (G minor) in the fifth bar. As well as this important movement there is an important corner to observe at bars 12 and 13. This is a II-V-I to F major and is the only part of the sequence that doesn't sound dark and minor. Here are a couple of simple piano voicings for this cadence to help you identify and hear it.

Track 14: II-V-I to F major

use of notes from the blues scale in the sample solo. Here is the D blues scale written out for you to learn.

D blues scale

You can negotiate all three of these chords melodically by using the F major scale throughout. Notice how the sample solo at this point also outlines important chord tones in the melodic line.

Another harmonic device that crops up several times is the minor II-V-I to D minor;

| Em$^{7(\flat 5)}$ / A$^{7(\flat 9 \flat 13)}$ / | Dmin^7 / / / |

Again here is a simple piano voicing for this progression to help you identify and hear it.

 Track 15: II-V-I to D minor

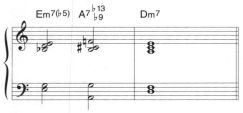

This cadence is a way of reinforcing the return to D minor and helps to outline the form. Try aiming for the important chord tones at this point if you want to be descriptive of the harmony. You can develop this later on by using the scales written out below the sample solo.

As already mentioned, the tempo and the chord changes are reminiscent of many blues sequences so you may like to experiment with the blues scale. See if you can identify the

" *... play clean and get to the pretty notes...* "
Charlie Parker

Summertime

Swing ♩ = 116

George Gershwin

Music and Lyrics by George Gershwin, Du Bose and
Dorothy Heyward and Ira Gershwin

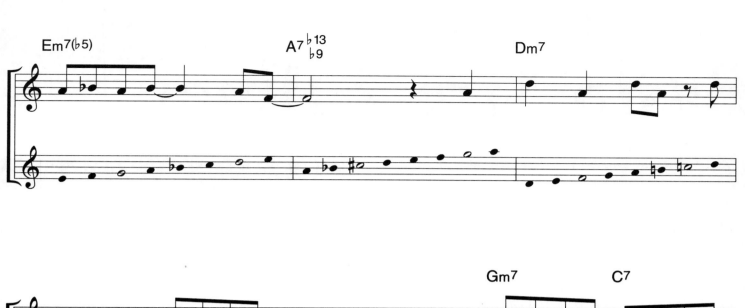

play 3 times then
D.%. al Coda

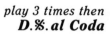

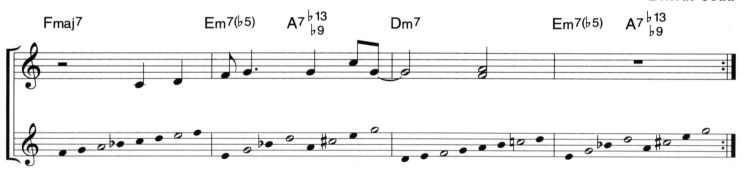

Rhythmic ideas for bars 1 and 2
of the Solo Section

Basin Street Blues

Spencer Williams

Basin Street Blues is one of the most enduring tunes from the early period of jazz. This style, known popularly as traditional jazz or just 'trad' for short, is still played by many bands today with a typical line up of piano, bass, drums and banjo as the rhythm section and a front line of clarinet, trumpet and trombone. Many of these early 'trad' tunes are characterised by a call-and-response theme followed by a riff based melody, as indeed is this one.

The composer, Spencer Williams, was born in New Orleans in 1889, and like many of his contemporaries moved to Chicago and then to New York at the turn of the century. He became very active in the thriving music scene at this time and as well as writing *Basin Street Blues* wrote many important tunes including *I Ain't Got Nobody*, *I Found A New Baby* and *Squeeze Me*, the last of which he co-wrote with pianist Fats Waller.

The Arrangement

This piece can be seen as having two main sections of 16 bars each. The first is at letter A and is basically a call-and-response between the lead player and the rest of the band. The second section, at letter B, is a melody made up from one simple rhythmic idea, broken up by a descending phrase at the end of the first eight bars.

Track 18: Call-and-response Theme

Track 19: Simple rhythmic idea

The Soloing

Traditionally, the soloing takes place over the second section rather than the first, making a 16 bar sequence to be repeated round and round. As with many trad jazz standards, the harmonic interest is in the series of dominant chord shapes moving round the cycle of fifths. Tunes like *Sweet Georgia Brown* and *Caravan* use this same device and are a useful cross-reference. Notice how the scale choices, printed out below the sample solo, change each bar by one accidental. A useful way to hear the harmonic movement in this sequence is to plot the guide tones as shown in the example below.

Play through the guide tones along with the recording and get used to hearing this linear route through the harmony as you solo. This will help you pick out the important notes in each of the chord changes as they go by. Look at the sample solo and see how the melody arrives at important chord tones just at the right place. Try to do this in your own solo.

To learn how to do this try taking a solo using just the given guide tones. See if you can create melodic ideas by playing these notes in varying ways, and then start to ornament them with the occasional passing note.

Once you feel comfortable with this stage, start to apply the scale types written underneath the chords. This will give you more scope melodically and really get you improvising lines.

If you listen to any traditional jazz recordings you will notice that quite often a front line instrument will be playing a guide tone line to accompany another soloist. Along with picking out some of the root movement, this is the typical role of the trombone in this sort of band. See if you can accompany the soloist on the recording in a similar way.

" ... if it sounds good and you like it, it doesn't matter if you break the rules, the ear is the final court of appeal..."

Stan Getz

Suggested listening...

Here is a list of recordings that are relevant to this piece. This is not an exhaustive or comprehensive list, but it will give you a starting point.

LOUIS ARMSTRONG
LOUIS ARMSTRONG VOL 1 - 1925-1932 (CLASSICS) 6 CD SET

LOUIS ARMSTRONG
LOUIS ARMSTRONG PLAYS WC HANDY (CBS)

LOUIS ARMSTRONG
SATCH PLAYS FATS (CBS)

FATS WALLER
JAZZ CLASSICS - FATS WALLER - 1927-34 (BBC)

FATS WALLER
TURN ON THE HEAT (RCA-BLUEBIRD)

Basin Street Blues

Spencer Williams

By Spencer Williams

Medium swing ♩ = 112

© 1929 & 1999 Triangle Music Co Inc, USA
EMI Music Publishing Ltd, London WC2H 0EA

Now's The Time

Charlie Parker is without doubt one of the most important figures in the development of jazz music. Together with Dizzy Gillespie he pioneered what became known as the 'be-bop' style of playing which took jazz into a whole new harmonic and rhythmic territory. This new music, which was considered quite avant-garde at the time, used a melodic language that was fully chromatic and yet maintained a strong blues reference. *Now's The Time* is a good example of this as it is really just a riff based blues Head, but still captures many of the defining stylistic elements of 'be-bop'.

The Arrangement

The beauty of this Head is that once you have learnt the first phrase you have virtually learnt the whole thing. Look at this first phrase and see how it is used throughout the rest of the tune. It is either repeated with a gap in between or repeated round and round as in the third and fourth bar.

Most composers will use repetition to create a sense of coherence in their writing and, generally speaking, to make the tune more catchy and memorable. However, repetition can become boring unless some sort of variation or fresh material is introduced. This is exactly what happens in the fifth and sixth bars. The pattern of repetition breaks here to outline a voice leading through the harmony. This is very much a characteristic of 'be-bop'. Notice how a chromatic line of B♭ to B♮ to C is brought out by the melody. It is no accident that these notes will also help you hear the important diminished chord in bar 6 of the

sequence when you come to improvise.

After this brief departure from the main melodic motif we see a return to it in bars 7 and 8. Then follows a blues phrase in bar 9. Remember that blues ideas work well throughout the entire 12-bars because the blues scale is a strong and recognisable melodic resource which you can superimpose over the harmonic sequence. It should not be surprising then, that much use of blues can sound quite harsh and dissonant. Bar 9 is a good example. Here we have a bluesy A♭ played over a G minor chord. These sort of pungent dissonances should not be shied away from but played with conviction and confidence. This is all part of the blues sound.

To round off the Head, Parker finishes with some purely rhythmic ideas. Look at the last two bars. These rhythmic placements are typical figures that a rhythm section might play behind a soloist.

Track 22: Rhythmic figure

As we can see, *Now's The Time* is a great tune to add to your repertoire as a jazz musician. It contains riffing, voice leading, good use of blues and characteristic rhythm section figures.

The Soloing

Being a 12-bar blues, you will find that you can use a combination of Mixolydian scales and the blues scale as melodic resources. A classic 12-bar sequence such as this is basically a harmonic journey through the tonic, subdominant, dominant and back to the tonic at the end. See if you can identify these harmonic landmarks in this blues in F. They will help you to identify them in your improvisations and so allow you to play the form of the blues as well as just stylistic elements.

The only difference between this and other blues sequences in this book is that this one has a diminished chord as a passing chord at bar six and the dominant at bar nine is represented by a II-V cadence of Gm to C7.

In the sample solo, notice the type of rhythmic vocabulary used. Many phrases start on an off beat to add to the syncopated nature of the music, and there is much use of space to break up the structure of the phrases. You can use all of these ideas in your own improvisations.

Charlie Parker

William Gottlieb

Suggested listening...

Here is a list of recordings that are relevant to this piece. This is not an exhaustive or comprehensive list, but it will give you a starting point.

CHARLIE PARKER (LASERLIGHT)
THE BEST OF BIRD

CHARLIE PARKER
THE ULTIMATE CHARLIE PARKER (VERVE/PGD)

CHARLIE PARKER
THE COMPLETE CHARLIE PARKER ON DIA
(JAZZ CLASSICS - CITY HALL - 4 CD SET)

" ... music is your own experience, your thoughts your wisdom. If you don't live it, it won't come out of your horn..."
Charlie Parker

Now's The Time

Charlie Parker

By Charlie Parker

Be-bop swing ♩ = 138

Henry Mancini

Peter Gunn Theme

If you've seen the movie 'The Blues Brothers', starring John Belushi and Dan Ackroyd, then you've heard the famous *Peter Gunn Theme* by Henry Mancini. This is one of the most memorable tracks from the movie. Other famous tunes from this cult film include *Gimme Some Lovin'*, *Shake A Tail Feather*, *Minnie The Moocher*, and *Sweet Home Chicago*. The last two of these titles are also featured in the second book in this series, so you'll be able to play along with these too. The soundtrack for the film has a star-studded line up that includes Ray Charles, Aretha Franklin and James Brown. Incidentally, the guitarist on the soundtrack is Steve Cropper, the same guitarist who features on *Green Onions*.

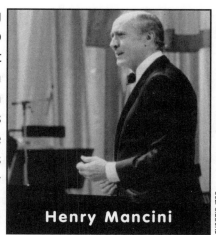

Suzi Gibbons

Henry Mancini

After the soloing there is a recap of the Head that leads to a coda section. Again the coda makes much use of the dramatic falls and eventually builds up to the climax of the whole piece by aggressively repeating a fall three bars from the end. Watch out for the rall and feel free to improvise over the last pause with the rest of the band.

The Arrangement

This piece has a repeated bass line throughout. The harmony stays on F^7 making this one of the easiest tunes to solo on in the series. As with the soundtrack, you have two bars of drums and four bars of rhythm section before you come in with the tune. Listen out for a drum fill and the following bass line before you come in. This will help you keep your place.

The actual tune is very dramatic with plenty of hard accents and stylistic inflections. Don't be afraid to really go for the swoops and falls marked on the part. Pay particular attention to whether you play notes long or short, especially the quavers. Listen carefully and in detail to the demonstration track. Developing your ear for phrasing and articulation will help your improvisations as well.

The Soloing

This is one style where nothing but the blues scale sounds great. There is also a minor pentatonic on which the blues scale is based that will work well here. It is worth spending a bit of time out practising a few patterns in this key. Giving yourself some dexterity with the melodic resources always improves your improvising as it allows you to think on your feet and be more spontaneous.

Track 25: Blues scale

F minor pentatonic   Blues scale

Notice in the sample solo how much space there is between the melodic ideas. Using space in your solo helps the listener take in what you have played and allows the rhythm section to interact with you by filling that space. It also gives you time to think of something good to play.

Although the soloing on this tune is made easier by the fact that there is only one chord throughout, you may consequently find it difficult to keep your place. With the same bass line over and over it is difficult to hear the landmarks that help you know where you are. The solo form is in fact divided into 16 bar sections, which in turn can be broken down into eight bar sections and four bar sections. Listen out for the drummer who will be marking out the form with appropriate fills. These will be your landmarks to help you keep your bearings while soloing.

Lastly, remember that there is nothing introverted about this style of playing. You are going to have to let your hair down and join in. In the words of James Brown, the Funky President himself, "Get up, Get into it, and Get involved!!!"

Suggested listening...

Here is a list of recordings that are relevant to this piece. This is not an exhaustive or comprehensive list, but it will give you a starting point.

VARIOUS ARTISTS   (ATLANTIC)
THE BLUES BROTHERS
MUSIC FROM THE SOUNDTRACK

JAMES BROWN   (POLYDOR)
FUNKY PRESIDENT
THE VERY BEST OF JAMES BROWN - VOL 1 & 2

" ... don't play what's there, play what's not there. Don't play what you know, play what you don't know... "

Miles Davis

Peter Gunn Theme

Henry Mancini

By Henry Mancini

Rock ♩ = 112

Solos

F7

F minor Pentatonic

Blues Scale

Coda

rall.

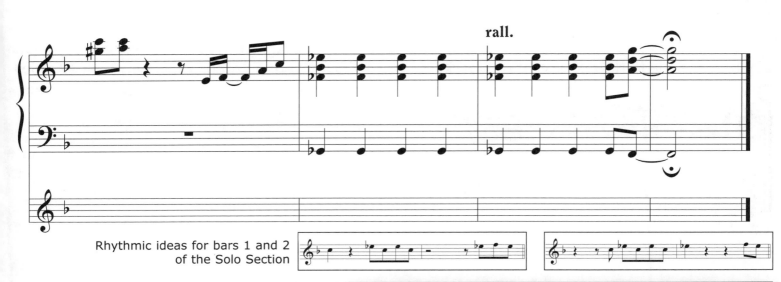

Rhythmic ideas for bars 1 and 2
of the Solo Section

Watermelon Man

Herbie Hancock is one of the most important jazz pianists of our time. As well as *Watermelon Man* he has composed many important jazz standards such as *Maiden Voyage*, *Dolphin Dance* and *Cantaloupe Island*. In his early twenties he was already on the road to establishing himself as a leading and innovating rhythm section player through his work with the Miles Davis Quintet. These collaborations with bassist Ron Carter and drummer Tony Williams in the mid '60s were to bring the role of the rhythm section on to a new level of interaction and communication that is the bench mark for all jazz players today.

Watermelon Man was written in 1962 for Herbie's debut album under his own name called *Takin' Off*. It is basically an extended version of a blues sequence with a funky straight quaver feel. What has now become a famous piano riff is at the centre of the rhythm section, while a strong bluesy tune is played over the top. Watch out for the rhythm section 'stop' on beat one of bar 14. This provides a break for you to throw in your best blues licks!

The Arrangement

There is a four bar introduction before you come in to allow you to get into the groove. Listen to the piano riff and see how it works rhythmically.

Track 28: Piano riff

The Head uses a lot of repeated ideas but always in a slightly different context. At bar 14 make sure that you play that F on beat one squarely with the rhythm section. This is known as a 'stop' and acts as a climax to the tune and sets up the last phrase.

The Soloing

As mentioned before, this is basically an extended blues sequence. It still uses the tonic, subdominant and dominant chord relationships as the other blues sequences in this book, but instead of a 12-bar format we have one of 16 bars. Let's look at this in more detail.

An ordinary 12-bar blues sequence can be seen as three lots of four bar groups, the first four bars starting on chord I, the second four on chord IV and the last four bars on chord V. These last four bars usually see a return to the home key via a V-IV-I type of cadence before returning to the top of the sequence.

Track 29: Last four bars

This is where *Watermelon Man* differs from a normal 12-bar blues. The move to the dominant in this extended sequence is prolonged by hovering around that chord V to IV movement before finally resolving to the home key at bar 15.

Here is the last eight bars of the *Watermelon Man* sequence to compare with the last four bars of an ordinary blues.

Track 30: Last eight bars

C7	B♭7	C7	B♭7
V Dominant	IV Subdominant	V Dominant	IV Subdominant

C7	B♭7	F7	F7
V Dominant	IV Subdominant	I Tonic	

As this is essentially a blues sequence you are at liberty to use the blues scale throughout, as well as the Mixolydian scales written out below the sample solo. Also notice the importance of the guide tones. These are the third and seventh degree of each chord type and are shown by the open note-heads in the written out scales. They will help you aim for the defining notes in each chord which will make your improvised melodies outline the chord changes.

"... it's important to find out what makes you want to play. And then when you play, your playing is going to have that joy, fascination and inquisitiveness..."

Iain Ballamy

Suggested listening...

Here is a list of recordings that are relevant to this piece. This is not an exhaustive or comprehensive list, but it will give you a starting point.

HERBIE HANCOCK (BLUE NOTE)
TAKIN' OFF

HERBIE HANCOCK (BLUE NOTE)
EMPYREAN ISLES

LEE MORGAN (BLUE NOTE)
THE SIDEWINDER

MILES DAVIS (COLUMBIA)
E.S.P.

HERBIE HANCOCK (COLUMBIA)
THRUST

HERBIE HANCOCK
SPEAK LIKE A CHILD (BLUE NOTE)

HERBIE HANCOCK
THE BEST OF HERBIE HANCOCK (BLUE NOTE)

Watermelon Man

Herbie Hancock

By Herbie Hancock

Rock shuffle ♩ = 120

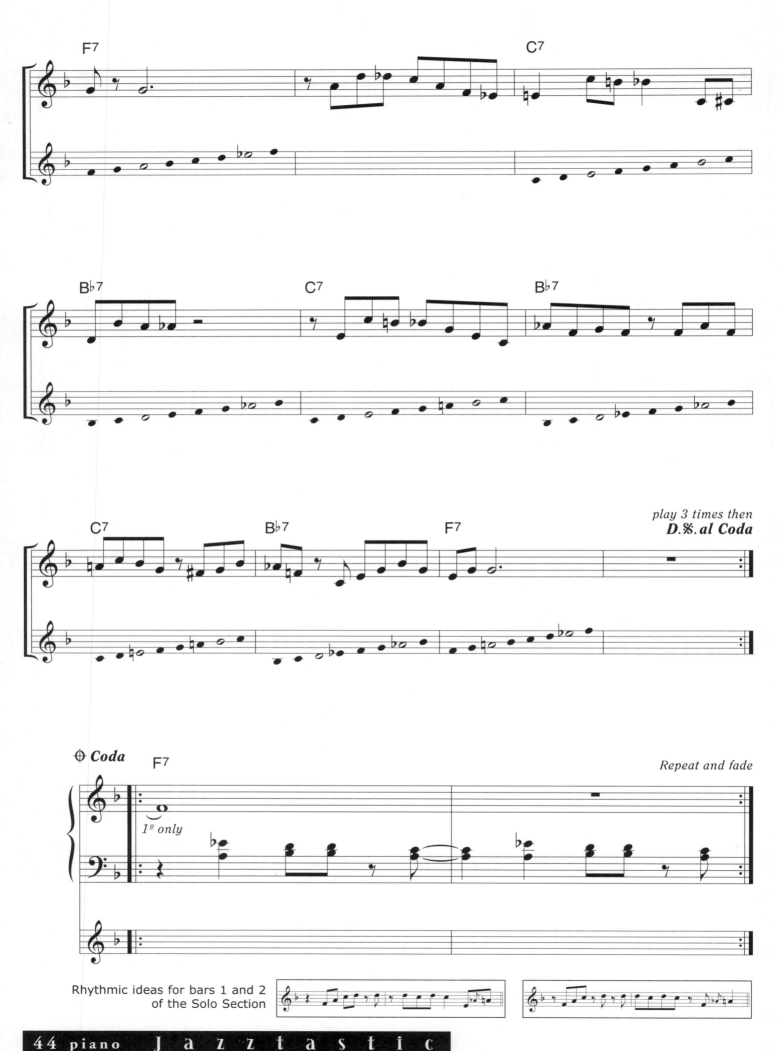

Printed and bound in Great Britain by Caligraving Limited 12/99